A LESSON BEFORE DYING

BY ROMULUS LINNEY

BASED ON THE NOVEL
BY ERNEST J. GAINES

DRAMATISTS
PLAY SERVICE
INC.

A LESSON BEFORE DYING
Copyright © 1998, 2001, Romulus Linney

All Rights Reserved

SPECIAL NOTE

A LESSON BEFORE DYING
A Play by Romulus Linney
Based on the Novel by Ernest J. Gaines

New York premiere produced by
Signature Theatre Company, New York City
James Houghton, Founding Artistic Director
Bruce Whitacre, Managing Director

A LESSON BEFORE DYING was commissioned by the
Alabama Shakespeare Festival
Kent Thompson, Artistic Director
Montgomery, Alabama

SPECIAL NOTE ON SONGS AND RECORDINGS

A LESSON BEFORE DYING was commissioned from the playwright by The Alabama Shakespeare Festival (Kent Thompson, Artistic Director) with the participation of Ernest J. Gaines, the author of the novel. It opened there on January 21, 2000. It was directed by Kent Thompson.

A LESSON BEFORE DYING received its New York premiere at the Peter Norton Space by The Signature Theatre Company (James Houghton, Founding Artistic Director; Bruce Whitacre, Managing Director) on September 17, 2000. It was directed by Kent Thompson; the set design was by Marjorie Bradley Kellogg; the lighting design was by Jane Cox; the costume design was by Alvin B. Perry; the original music was by Chic Street Man; the sound design was by Don Tindall; the production stage manager was Francys Olivia Burch. The cast was as follows:

EMMA GLEN .... Beatrice Winde
PAUL BONIN .... Aaron Harpold
GRANT WIGGINS .... Isiah Whitlock, Jr.
SAM GUIDRY .... Stephen Bradbury
JEFFERSON .... Jamahl Marsh
VIVIAN BAPTISTE .... Tracey A. Leigh
REVEREND MOSES AMBROSE .... John Henry Redwood
CHILDREN'S VOICES provided by Mr. Michael Clayton's third-grade class, Patterson Elementary School, Montgomery, Alabama.

The playwright is grateful to Melissa Maxwell, Barbara Meek, Robert Colston, Vicki Smith, Terry Cernak and Sara Lee Howell for their invaluable participation in the Alabama Shakespeare Festival production.

CHARACTERS
(in order of appearance)

PAUL BONIN
EMMA GLENN
GRANT WIGGINS
SAM GUIDRY
JEFFERSON
VIVIAN BAPTISTE
THE REVEREND MOSES AMBROSE
CHILDREN'S VOICES

PLACE

Bayonne, Louisiana. A storeroom in the Parish Courthouse. A table in the Rainbow Club. A schoolroom. A bench in front of the Courthouse.

TIME

1948.

A LESSON BEFORE DYING

ACT ONE

Above the stage is a device that says in large letters: "Bayonne, Louisiana, 1948." It remains throughout the play. Beneath this device, and around the stage, are walls of red brick, dusty from the turn of the century. They are the kind of bricks that make up a Parish Courthouse in Bayonne, Louisiana. At stage center, dominating everything, is a large platform. It is a storeroom in the Bayonne Courthouse. Boxes of records, seed sacks, a few old file cabinets, at rear. Some folding chairs, stacked. An upturned spare bench. An entrance stage left and another upstage right, with a hallway, or steps, leading on from offstage. An empty space at center. A tall window to one side. Downstage center, a worn public bench, sitting in front of the Courthouse. At right, a sign saying "Rainbow Club," a small table and two chairs. At left a table that serves as a desk in a classroom. Behind it, stands a worn American flag. The character of Grant Wiggins will move in plain sight, from one place to another throughout the play. Lights fade. A cold light shines weakly through the window of the storeroom. The door at left opens. Enter Paul Bonin, Deputy Sheriff, white, twenties.

PAUL. In here. *(Behind him comes Miss Emma Glenn, a woman in her seventies. She carries a handbag, a package wrapped in newspaper, and a wicker basket. Miss Emma looks around the bleak room. She sighs. Then, in discomfort but with determination, she stands waiting at the center of the room. Paul turns on some lights. He looks again at the frail old woman standing by herself and at the folded chairs. He starts to open up a folding chair for her, then stops himself. He is being*

5

polite but firm.) Sheriff said in here. You can sit down, if you like.

MISS EMMA. No, thank you.

PAUL. Is the preacher coming?

MISS EMMA. Not today. The teacher today.

PAUL. Teacher?

MISS EMMA. From the plantation school.

PAUL. Sheriff Guidry know about him?

MISS EMMA. Not yet.

PAUL. He'd better. He's not happy about any of it.

MISS EMMA. I know that.

PAUL. Please, you can sit down.

MISS EMMA. No, thank you.

PAUL. Suit yourself. *(Exit Paul. Miss Emma sighs. Her legs ache. She is in pain. She puts down the wicker basket. She looks at the folded chairs, but will not use one. She sighs, gathers herself, stands up straighter. She closes her eyes and prays.)*

MISS EMMA. The Lord is my Shepherd. I shall not want. He leadeth me beside the still waters. He restoreth my soul. *(The door opens.)*

PAUL'S VOICE. In there. *(Enter Grant Wiggins, an man in his twenties, wearing neat but worn clothes. The door closes behind him. Miss Emma opens her eyes.)*

MISS EMMA. So you came.

GRANT. You think I wouldn't?

MISS EMMA. Jefferson on trial, you didn't come. You forgot about him.

GRANT. Miss Emma, that boy is going to die.

MISS EMMA. You think he did it.

GRANT. It doesn't make any difference what I think!

MISS EMMA. He is innocent!

GRANT. All right!

MISS EMMA. Could you open up a chair so I can sit down?

GRANT. He wouldn't give you a chair?

MISS EMMA. I never asked him for one. I'm asking you. *(Grant opens up two folding chairs for them. Miss Emma sits heavily, in pain. Grant sits beside her.)*

GRANT. Miss Emma, Jefferson is as good as dead.

MISS EMMA. I know that.

GRANT. There was a trial. The verdict was guilty. I teach school. I can't raise the dead.

MISS EMMA. I know that, too.

GRANT. All I can do is try to keep others from ending up like he did.

MISS EMMA. How hard?

GRANT. Ma'am?

MISS EMMA. How hard you try for others here?

GRANT. As hard as I can!

MISS EMMA. Which ain't much!

GRANT. Why are you insulting me?

MISS EMMA. Why not? Who took you in? From the road, from the *dirt?*

GRANT. My Aunt Lou.

MISS EMMA. Who brung you up?

GRANT. Tante Lou.

MISS EMMA. When nobody else cared if you lived or if you died, who fed you?

GRANT. She did!

MISS EMMA. And who was her friend? Who else put grits in your mouth? Who else mended one pair pants while you wore the othern? Who saved dollars and nickels and dimes *and* pennies, so you could go to that college?

GRANT. You did! I don't deny it!

MISS EMMA. You try to! Like right now! But I'm not letting you. You owe me something, Mister Schoolteacher!

GRANT. You asking me to save his life?

MISS EMMA. No.

GRANT. Then what do you want me to do?

MISS EMMA. They called him a hog.

GRANT. Called him a what?

MISS EMMA. You'd know if you'd been at the trial.

GRANT. Who called Jefferson a hog? *(Door opens. Enter Paul.)*

PAUL. You want to see Sheriff Guidry, you got to do it now.

MISS EMMA. All right. *(Enter, slowly and with distaste, Sam Guidry, Sheriff of Bayonne. He is a large, intelligent, impressive man. Though he wears cowboy boots and carries a wide-brimmed hat, he is dressed in a handsome suit. He greets Miss Emma.)*

SHERIFF GUIDRY. Miss Emma. *(He sees Grant.)* Who's this?

PAUL. She wants him here.

MISS EMMA. Grant Wiggins is teacher at the plantation school.

SHERIFF GUIDRY. What is he doing here?

MISS EMMA. I want him to see my boy Jefferson.

SHERIFF GUIDRY. *(To Grant.)* You kin to the prisoner?

GRANT. No, sir.

SHERIFF GUIDRY. What's in there?

MISS EMMA. Clean clothes in the package. Food in the basket.

SHERIFF GUIDRY. In the first place, the prisoner is not your son. He's your godson. In the second, this is no place for a picnic. What's your name again, Professor?

GRANT. Grant Wiggins, sir.

SHERIFF GUIDRY. Can I teach you something, Professor?

GRANT. Yes, sir.

SHERIFF GUIDRY. Miss Emma calls up my wife. She can't meet Jefferson in his jail cell because it is too cramped. Day Room, too many people. How about that?

GRANT. I don't know, Sheriff.

SHERIFF GUIDRY. You sure? Sure you don't know she told my wife we owe it to her? Anything like that?

GRANT. No, sir.

SHERIFF GUIDRY. Did you put her up to this?

GRANT. No, sir!

SHERIFF GUIDRY. Then my wife calls me on the phone. I say, they can use this storeroom. But now that isn't enough. She wants some schoolteacher to counsel the convict, too. What do you think about that?

GRANT. I think it's up to you, Sheriff.

SHERIFF GUIDRY. That's right, it is. A man to be executed is in my personal custody. I decide and the answer is no. Professor, get out of here. *(Miss Emma has opened her purse. She takes out a piece of paper with a telephone number written on it and puts a hand on Grant's arm, keeping him there.)*

MISS EMMA. I called this number. *(Miss Emma holds out a piece of paper to Sheriff Guidry.)*

SHERIFF GUIDRY. Did you hear me, Professor?

MISS EMMA. Phone number.

SHERIFF GUIDRY. What?

MISS EMMA. Henri Pichot *and* his wife. They both waiting to hear from you. *(Sheriff Guidry takes the paper.)*

SHERIFF GUIDRY. You called him?

MISS EMMA. And his wife. I was with the Pichot family a long time, and you know it.

SHERIFF GUIDRY. You are pushing me very hard.

MISS EMMA. Call Mr. and Mrs. Pichot. They waiting.

SHERIFF GUIDRY. God damn it. *(To Paul.)* Come on. *(Exeunt Sheriff Guidry and Paul.)*

GRANT. Henri Pichot?

MISS EMMA. I worked for those people near thirty years. How many their babies I hold in these arms? How many clothes I wash? How many meals I serve? Who ran Pichot house when there was divorces and deaths in that family? Who carried law papers to the Court House and flowers to the graveyard? I did all kinds of things for the Henri Pichots and Sam Guidry's wife is a Pichot. They'll do what I want.

GRANT. And what is that, Miss Emma?

MISS EMMA. It was Jefferson's own lawyer called him a hog.

GRANT. The public defender. Why?

MISS EMMA. He saw the verdict was go'n be guilty. So he says, "Look at this boy. What kind of justice is this? Backwoods Louisiana. Dirt poor. Knows nothing, is nothing. Not even a human being. I would as soon put a hog in that electric chair. Because that's what we will be doing, electrocuting a hog." That's what was said, before all the world, while you wasn't there! Now Jefferson don't say nothing, except yes, all right, he's a hog, and they can drag him to that chair and kill him like a hog. That's what he's go'n make them do. *(Enter Sheriff Guidry and Paul.)*

SHERIFF GUIDRY. Pichot family says yes. I say, within the law.

MISS EMMA. The law going to kill Jefferson, Mr. Guidry! I accept that!

SHERIFF GUIDRY. Then what do you want done here?

MISS EMMA. Grant Wiggins is a teacher.

SHERIFF GUIDRY. So?

MISS EMMA. I want him to teach my Jefferson to die like a man!

SHERIFF GUIDRY. Wiggins, what is this?

9

GRANT. Evidently the defense called Jefferson a hog.

SHERIFF GUIDRY. What can you say to Jefferson about that?

GRANT. I have no idea. *(Pause.)* Sir.

SHERIFF GUIDRY. Folks. Let a preacher visit Jefferson, the way it ought to be. Think about his soul now, not his body.

MISS EMMA. The Reverend Ambrose will visit Jefferson. This something else. I'd 'preciate a answer.

SHERIFF GUIDRY. I'll consider it.

MISS EMMA. 'Preciate it now.

SHERIFF GUIDRY. *What?*

MISS EMMA. If it ain't too much a bother!

SHERIFF GUIDRY. Well, it is! But all right. Thank the Pichot family for this, not me. You, the preacher, and Wiggins see the prisoner. In here. Both doors locked, him in shackles and leg chains. One hour, weekdays, not before three and not after five. And nobody gets upset. First sign of aggravation, any trouble at all, it's finished. Paul, take over. *(Exit Sheriff Guidry.)*

PAUL. Wait here. *(Exit Paul. Miss Emma sits down, weakly.)*

MISS EMMA. *(Softly.)* Thank you, Lord. *(Grant takes a chair and sits by her.)*

GRANT. Your legs hurt?

MISS EMMA. Yes, but I got it done.

GRANT. Not yet, you haven't. What about me?

MISS EMMA. You?

GRANT. You never asked if I want to do this.

MISS EMMA. I knowed what you'd say. No.

GRANT. You talk to Jefferson. Why should I?

MISS EMMA. Think I haven't tried? He won't even look at me. My boy just look at the wall, say nothing. You the teacher. You got to talk to him!

GRANT. Miss Emma, I do not! It has been a long time.

MISS EMMA. Six short years!

GRANT. Six long years!

MISS EMMA. Went to a college? Got a degree?

GRANT. I said it a thousand times! Thank you!

MISS EMMA. But what you mean?

GRANT. Never mind.

MISS EMMA. No, what you mean?!

10

GRANT. I mean I hate teaching! I hate the South! I hate everything about this place! Before I go crazy, I'm going to live somewhere else!

MISS EMMA. Not here!

GRANT. No, ma'am!

MISS EMMA. Not with your own people here?

GRANT. No, ma'am!

MISS EMMA. Or the children?

GRANT. The children? They don't like me. I don't like them. What's called a school here is pitiful waste of everybody's time! I try! I teach! And I get next to nothing taught to anybody.

MISS EMMA. Try harder.

GRANT. No thank you. As for Jefferson, none of this is going to help him. And I haven't said I am doing any of it.

MISS EMMA. They coming back. *(A light on the long corridor leading to the storeroom. Paul is leading Jefferson, a young African American man, in handcuffs and leg chains, awkwardly down the corridor. Paul brings Jefferson into the storeroom. Jefferson wears green prison overalls. Paul locks the corridor door.)*

PAUL. *(To Jefferson.)* Stand right there. *(To Grant and Miss Emma.)* Stand up. *(They do.)* Purse. *(Miss Emma hands him her purse, which he searches and returns to her.)* Package. Basket. *(Paul opens the package, and examines the clothes. Same with the basket. To Grant.)* Pockets. *(Grant displays the contents of his pockets.)* Turn around. Arms out. *(Paul searches him thoroughly.)* No knives, no forks, no plates. No hatpins, no pocketknives, no ice picks, and no razor blades. One hour. Knock if you want out earlier. *(Exit Paul, at left, locking that door as well. Jefferson doesn't move. He just stands there in chains, staring ahead. He will not look at them.)*

MISS EMMA. Jefferson. *(No response.)* How you feel, Jefferson? *(No response.)* Get him a chair. *(Grant takes one of the folding chairs and puts it close to Jefferson. Jefferson tries to sit and his leg chains get in the way. Grant tries to help Jefferson. Jefferson sits.)* Jefferson? *(No response.)* I brung Professor Wiggins. I brung you fried chicken, yams, and tea cakes. *(No response.)* Ain't you going to ask me to sit with you, Jefferson? *(Grant gets her a chair and puts her next to Jefferson. She lays out the clothes before him.)* Here's pants, your brown shirt, long johns and two pair of socks. All washed clean. *(No response.)* Ain't you going to speak to me, Jefferson? Give me

11

the basket. *(Miss Emma touches him, gently.)* You just want to talk to me? You want Professor Wiggins to go? *(No response. Grant hands her the food.)* Look what I brung you. You like my fried chicken. Yams and tea cakes.

JEFFERSON. Don't matter.

MISS EMMA. What?

JEFFERSON. I said don't matter.

MISS EMMA. It matter to me. You matter to me.

JEFFERSON. Chicken, yams, tea cakes. Don't matter.

MISS EMMA. Yeah, they do, Jefferson. Here. *(Miss Emma takes a small bite of chicken.)* Nothing wrong with this. You always liked my chicken. *(Silence.)* You want a yam? A tea cake?

JEFFERSON. You the one?

GRANT. What?

JEFFERSON. Go'n jeck that switch?

MISS EMMA. That's Professor Wiggins, your teacher. What switch? *(Jefferson slaps his chair and makes a loud buzz, like electricity.)*

JEFFERSON. What fries a hog!

MISS EMMA. Oh, my boy! *(Miss Emma starts toward him. He turns his back on her, slams down his feet and his shackles.)*

JEFFERSON. I don't want you here!

MISS EMMA. Yes, you do! I want to help you!

JEFFERSON. Get her out of here!

MISS EMMA. Jefferson! *(To Grant.)* Say something to him!

GRANT. Jefferson.

JEFFERSON. Both of you! Leave me alone!

MISS EMMA. Oh, my boy! Jefferson!

JEFFERSON. Can't you leave me alone? *(Miss Emma tries to hold Jefferson, but he breaks away from her.)* All right! Knock for the man! *(Grant knocks on the door.)*

MISS EMMA. All right! But we're not through. We'll be back, with the Reverend Ambrose. *(The door opens. Enter Paul.)*

PAUL. That didn't take long.

MISS EMMA. Can I leave the food and the clothes?

PAUL. I suppose so.

MISS EMMA. If he don't want it, can you give it to others in the jailhouse?

PAUL. I suppose. *(Paul take Jefferson out, closing the door on Miss*

12

Emma.)
MISS EMMA. We'll be back, Jefferson! We go'n make you feel better! *(The door closes in her face. She puts her hands against the door.)* Oh, Lord Jesus! Stand by me! *(Lights, music. Exit Miss Emma, then Grant. Lights fade. A dim light on the table and flag at stage left. Voices of children are heard.)*
CHILDREN'S VOICES. I pledge allegiance to the flag of the United States of America, and to the Republic for which it stands. One nation, indivisible, with liberty and justice for all. *(Lights up on the table, which is a desk. A flimsy blackboard behind it. At its side, a worn American flag, on a pole. Enter Grant. He carries a cardboard box. He sits at his table/desk. He speaks to his pupils in front of him.)*
GRANT. I have a few things to say before we begin classes. First, when you write a simple sentence, it doesn't slant up or down. It stays on a straight line. *(He takes a small package out of the cardboard box.)* Second, we are wasting chalk. The school board gave me what they say is enough for the year. It's about gone. When it runs out, they're not giving us any more. *(He puts that back and takes out two battered textbooks.)* Third, these hand-me-down textbooks from the white schools are fragile. You don't have to tear them apart, they come apart. So when they have pages gone, or torn out of them, find someone whose book has that page. When some pages are stuck together, with paste, or chewing gum, don't tear the pages apart. Pull gently or let me do it. We can't get other books. *(He puts them back.)* And fourth. For some of you, it's ladybug time in class. You sit playing with bugs. You think that's why I'm here, so that you can play with bugs? Do you know what is going on in Bayonne right now? Do you know what is going to happen to someone just like you? Who sat right where you are sitting now, only a few years ago? You all know who I'm talking about. Jefferson. They are going to kill him in Bayonne. They are going to sit him in a chair. They're going to tie him down with straps. They're going to connect wires to his head, to his wrists, to his legs, and they're going to shoot electricity into his body, until he is dead. What does that have to do with you? It's exactly what I am trying to stop, right here right now. I'm trying to make you responsible young men and young ladies, who don't wind up where Jefferson is. But you, you refuse to study! You won't write a straight sentence! You'll be playing with *bugs* the

day Jefferson — *(Grant stops himself.)* Does this make any sense to you? Does it? All right. Arithmetic. Let's go to work. *(Lights fade. Lights come up on stage left: the Rainbow Club. Vivian Baptiste, a beautiful woman of thirty, is sitting at a table, grading schoolwork. Low music. Enter Grant, with two beers. He is upset and distracted.)* Hey.

VIVIAN. Hey. *(He puts the beers down in front of them.)*

GRANT. Where you been?

VIVIAN. Shopping. I heard there was a sale at Edwin's.

GRANT. Get anything?

VIVIAN. No. The sale was on radios, not clothes.

GRANT. Well. Drink up.

VIVIAN. You all right?

GRANT. Cheers.

VIVIAN. Cheers. *(They sip their beer.)* Helen and James say we can use their house in Baton Rouge. They can go to dinner and a movie while we're there.

GRANT. You want to do that again?

VIVIAN. No, but what else?

GRANT. We can go to my place.

VIVIAN. I can't do that. I can't be seen living with you.

GRANT. Then go home, pack your clothes, get your children and let's go. Tonight.

VIVIAN. What?

GRANT. Let's get out of here!

VIVIAN. No.

GRANT. People do it all the time.

VIVIAN. They might, but we don't.

GRANT. And why don't we?

VIVIAN. Because there are other people involved! We have a commitment. To them!

GRANT. To do what? Teach children who don't want to learn?

VIVIAN. The children I teach do want to learn!

GRANT. Maybe yours, in town! Mine, in the country, sure don't! You teach in a building. I teach in a rundown, rotting away shack! And I am sick to death of it!

VIVIAN. How much you had to drink?

GRANT. A whole damn barrel of your commitment. Let's GO!

VIVIAN. I'll go, all right. Away from you!

14

GRANT. Wait!

VIVIAN. Not when you act like this!

GRANT. Vivian, I'm dead here! Somewhere else in this country we could be alive!

VIVIAN. That's what you say. Go. Run away. I am still married. A separation is not a divorce.

GRANT. The divorce is coming! I'll marry you the day it does. But I want to go now and I want you and the children to come with me.

VIVIAN. No. We have to be responsible for what we do.

GRANT. And you think I'm not? Damn this!

VIVIAN. Grant, what's happened to you?

GRANT. I've been to the Courthouse, that's what's happened. I've been to Miss Emma, *that's* what's happened!

VIVIAN. Miss Emma?

GRANT. It's Jefferson. The public defender called him a hog in court. So he is acting like one. Miss Emma says I have to change that. I have to teach him to die. Like a man. With — I don't know — strength, dignity, something! Well, who am I, God? I don't know how a man should live. How can I tell a man how he should die? What do I say to him?

VIVIAN. I don't know, but something. Miss Emma is right. You have to do your best.

GRANT. And why do I have to?

VIVIAN. For us, as well as for him. For Miss Emma, for everybody in town and for me. You don't turn away. You let people depend on you.

GRANT. You talk like Miss Emma.

VIVIAN. If I must!

GRANT. What's wrong with just leaving? I went to California once. I can do it again.

VIVIAN. Not with me.

GRANT. You won't go?

VIVIAN. Not that way. Run toward something, all right, but not run away. Take me, Grant. Not the road out of town.

GRANT. I'll think about it. What you said. *(They drink.)* What are you doing this weekend?

VIVIAN. Homework and housework.

GRANT. Want to go to Baton Rouge? I'll pay your cousin Dora to sit for you.

VIVIAN. Friday would be good. *(They drink. Lights fade. The door left opens. Enter Sheriff Sam Guidry. Behind him, with a straw basket of food, comes Grant.)*

SHERIFF GUIDRY. I want to talk to you. Arms out, feet out. *(Grant puts down the basket. Guidry searches him thoroughly.)* How you and my prisoner getting along?

GRANT. This'll be my first time alone with him.

SHERIFF GUIDRY. Where's his godmother?

GRANT. Home sick. She says.

SHERIFF GUIDRY. Is she or ain't she?

GRANT. She says she's got a cold, but I think she just wants me and Jefferson together.

SHERIFF GUIDRY. What's in the basket?

GRANT. Same as before.

SHERIFF GUIDRY. Picnics.

GRANT. Yes, sir. *(Sheriff Guidry finishes searching Grant.)*

SHERIFF GUIDRY. Get the basket. *(Grant picks up the basket.)* Just hold it there. *(Grant holds out the basket while Guidry, with a penknife, inspects it closely, and roughly, cutting open wrappings, etc.)* The idea is, you being a professor, you're going to make a man out of him?

GRANT. Something like that, sir.

SHERIFF GUIDRY. A man for what?

GRANT. His godmother asked me to talk to him. She didn't ask about what.

SHERIFF GUIDRY. I'm asking you. What are you going to talk about?

GRANT. I don't honestly know.

SHERIFF GUIDRY. You sure about that, Wiggins?

GRANT. Sir. It's her idea, not mine.

SHERIFF GUIDRY. That was not the question.

GRANT. What was? Sir?

SHERIFF GUIDRY. Make him a man for *what?*

GRANT. To die with dignity, I suppose.

SHERIFF GUIDRY. Some job.

GRANT. Yes, sir.

SHERIFF GUIDRY. But is it a good one? I mean, should it be

16

done at all?

GRANT. Hard to say.

SHERIFF GUIDRY. I don't like it, Professor. I never been to college but I learned a thing or two about life in this job. I have to execute this boy, not torture him. I would rather watch a dumb hog die in that chair than an upset, out of his mind, aggravated boy fry in it. I don't think you'll make him understand anything. How do you like that, Professor?

GRANT. I see your point.

SHERIFF GUIDRY. Nobody's heard from Jefferson's mother or the father?

GRANT. No, sir.

SHERIFF GUIDRY. Long gone God knows where and never coming back, huh?

GRANT. I suppose, sir.

SHERIFF GUIDRY. Can't blame them. Can you?

GRANT. I'm not blaming anybody for anything.

SHERIFF GUIDRY. How about you, Professor? Man smart as you are, why ain't you gone, too?

GRANT. People paid my way to college so I would come back and teach the children and that's what I'm doing. Sir.

SHERIFF GUIDRY. All your life? *(Pause.)* I said, all your life?

GRANT. Who knows?

SHERIFF GUIDRY. I do. You people are all the same. You'll be long gone, too. *(The corridor light comes on, and we hear the leg chains of Jefferson as Paul brings him down the corridor. Paul brings Jefferson into the storeroom. He locks the door behind them. Sheriff Guidry wipes his hands with his handkerchief, in distaste. To Paul.)* From now on, you do the search, then you get the boy.

PAUL. Yes, Sheriff. *(Sheriff Guidry takes a skeptical look at Jefferson.)*

SHERIFF GUIDRY. *(To Grant.)* No aggravation. He gets upset, it's over.

GRANT. Yes, sir. *(Exeunt Sheriff Guidry and Paul. Paul locks the door.)* Jefferson. *(No response.)* Jefferson, your Nannan couldn't make it today.

JEFFERSON. I see that.

GRANT. She's got a bad cold. That's hard when you're as old as she

17

is. But she made something for you to eat. She sent me to bring it to you. She hopes we can have a talk. *(Jefferson looks slowly up at Grant, then slowly back away, to the tall barred window. Grant goes to the window. There is more sunlight outside than before.)* You're looking out the window. See more than you can from your cell, I expect.

JEFFERSON. Part of a branch.

GRANT. That all?

JEFFERSON. Yeah.

GRANT. That's a sycamore out there. I can see blue between the branches. Can you see that from your cell? *(Jefferson nods, looks away, down at the floor.)* You hungry?

JEFFERSON. You brung some corn?

GRANT. Corn?

JEFFERSON. What hogs eat.

GRANT. Stop it, Jefferson. You are afraid and nobody can blame you. But come on. Some chicken in here. Biscuits and sweet potatoes. Look. Even some candy she made. Try it. Make your Nannan happy.

JEFFERSON. Hogs don't eat no candy.

GRANT. You're not a hog. You're a man. *(Jefferson turns away.)* Well, can *I* have a piece of chicken? I missed my lunch. *(No response, though Jefferson is watching Grant now. Grant eats some chicken and a nibble of a biscuit.)* Your Nannan sure can cook.

JEFFERSON. That's for youmans.

GRANT. You're human, Jefferson. Come on.

JEFFERSON. Youmans don't live in no stall. Slop and shit and old hog. I'm old hog you fattening up to kill. No? You come on.

GRANT. Saying things like that hurts your Nannan. You want me to tell her you said things like that?

JEFFERSON. Don't care what you tell her.

GRANT. When she cares so much?

JEFFERSON. Well, I don't.

GRANT. Don't what?

JEFFERSON. Care. About nothing. Old hog don't care 'bout nothing.

GRANT. But she does. And I do.

JEFFERSON. Y'all youmans.

GRANT. You're a man, Jefferson. Act like one.

18

JEFFERSON. Act like *what?*

GRANT. Like what you are.

JEFFERSON. What I am? Sho. *(Jefferson falls violently onto the basket of food. On his hands and knees, grunting like a pig, he eats, hands smacking the floor, smearing his face with food. He does this for a long time, savagely, ferociously. Jefferson looks up at Grant, a terrible grin on his food-smeared face. Then he jumps back to his feet.)* That's what I am! That's what they say I am! So that's what I'll be! Like a hog, they can drag me to that cher! I ain't walking! *(Grant puts away his food, slowly and carefully, with decorum.)*

GRANT. All right, Jefferson. But when I go back to your god-mother who cut this chicken and rolled these biscuits and sugared these pralines for you, I am going to tell her that you and I sat down like gentlemen and ate together. And I'll tell her how much you liked her food. Especially the pralines.

JEFFERSON. Go'n do that.

GRANT. Want to hurt me, Jefferson? Make me feel guilty because of what happened to you? Let's tell each other the truth. Do you want me to come back here? *(No response.)* The white man out there, he doesn't want me back here, that's for sure. He says I will never make you understand anything. But your Nannan doesn't think so. She wants us to talk. Now what do you want? You want your Nannan to lose and the white man to win? *(No response.)* Well, I brought you this, anyhow. A comb for your hair. Use it when you see your Nannan. Will you? *(No response. Grant puts the comb down in front of Jefferson.)* All right, Jefferson. No more. But let's stay the full hour. I damn well don't want that white sheriff thinking he's right and we're wrong. *(Jefferson shakes his head slightly.)* We'll just look at that sycamore tree, and the sky. How's that? *(Jefferson sits down again, facing the sycamore tree. Grant eats a praline. Jefferson takes the comb. Lights fade on them. Lights come up on the bench in front of the Courthouse. Miss Emma and the Reverend Moses Ambrose are waiting there. Moses Ambrose is a man in his fifties. As usual, Miss Emma carries a basket of food. Reverend Ambrose looks at a pocket watch. They wait. Enter Grant.)* Miss Emma. Reverend Ambrose. *(Reverend Ambrose gets up, shakes hands with Grant.)*

REVEREND AMBROSE. Grant.

MISS EMMA. 'Bout time, Grant.

GRANT. I'm glad to see you got over your cold. *(Grant sits on one of the benches.)*

MISS EMMA. I never had no cold. I wanted you and Jefferson to talk by yourselves. How was he?

GRANT. All right.

MISS EMMA. What y'all talk about?

GRANT. Different things. I think he'll use a comb I bought for him. I think he's okay.

MISS EMMA. What else? Whole hour, what else?

GRANT. I can't remember everything!

REVEREND AMBROSE. GOD! Did you talk about God?

GRANT. No, I didn't. I was with him about an hour, then I went back of town.

MISS EMMA. What for?

GRANT. I got a girl I meet there.

REVEREND AMBROSE. Did you say a girl, back of town?

MISS EMMA. Maybe that's where you spent all your time!

GRANT. If you don't think I went in that Courthouse jail, go in there and ask them!

MISS EMMA. Don't you get uppity with me!

GRANT. I'm not getting uppity with you! I spent an hour with him! I had a drumstick and a biscuit and he had I can't remember just what. We talked. I went back of town to see my girl. Exactly that!

REVEREND AMBROSE Grant.

GRANT Yes, sir?

REVEREND AMBROSE Deep in you.

GRANT Yes, sir?

REVEREND AMBROSE. Deep, deep in you, what you think?

GRANT. About what, Reverend?

REVEREND AMBROSE. You think he know the gravity?

GRANT. Gravity?

REVEREND AMBROSE. That he's going to die?

GRANT. He's not an idiot. Of course he knows he's going to die.

REVEREND AMBROSE. Don't talk to me like that! I mean the gravity of his soul!

GRANT. I don't know anything about his soul, Reverend Ambrose.

(Light on the corridor leading to the storeroom. Paul is bringing Jefferson

20

into the room while Moses Ambrose speaks.)
REVEREND AMBROSE. But I do. I have to. I am a minister of God. I was not educated in a college. I only read one book, the Holy Bible. But I hear God's voice. It says preach! Baptize! Visit the sick, comfort the suffering, and bury the dead. Now I have this boy, a living soul, in my care. I baptized him. Like I baptized you. Both of you. Why didn't you talk to him about God?
GRANT. We didn't get around to it.
REVEREND AMBROSE. Didn't get around to God?
GRANT. No, sir.
REVEREND AMBROSE. If you talking to a man about to *meet* God, what else is more important?
GRANT. That's where you come in, Reverend.
REVEREND AMBROSE. *(To Miss Emma.)* Why have you brought this man, this ungodly man, into this matter?
MISS EMMA. He's a teacher.
REVEREND AMBROSE. And I'm not?
GRANT. You want my place? Take it!
REVEREND AMBROSE. I ought to! Maybe he'd learn something!
MISS EMMA. My Lord! I wish you men understood each other better than you do, but you don't. So hush up and let's go. *(Lights out on the forestage. Light on Jefferson, in handcuffs and leg chains. He is seated on one of the folding chairs, looking at the floor. Lights come up on Miss Emma, Reverend Ambrose, and Grant standing in front of Jefferson.)*
REVEREND AMBROSE. Young man, I pray for you every night. The Lord is hearing my prayers. Here is His Word. Put your faith in Him and He will bring you through.
MISS EMMA. And eat something for me.
JEFFERSON. Sho. Got any corn?
MISS EMMA. Corn?
JEFFERSON. For a hog.
GRANT. Jefferson.
MISS EMMA. A hog, Jefferson? You ain't no hog, Jefferson.
JEFFERSON. Just th'ow it to me. I'll eat it.
GRANT. Jefferson, don't!!
MISS EMMA. I'll never th'ow nothing to you, Jefferson. You th'ow a bone to a dog. Slop to pigs. You ain't no hog.

21

JEFFERSON. Ain't I? *(Jefferson drops to his knees in front of Miss Emma.)* Feed the hog!

REVEREND AMBROSE. Stop that!

JEFFERSON. He'll eat for you! What you want, ain't it?

MISS EMMA. Jefferson!

JEFFERSON. Go on! Fatten him up!

MISS EMMA. Jefferson, behave!!

JEFFERSON. Feed the hog, so you can fry him in that cher! *(Miss Emma slaps Jefferson hard in the face.)*

GRANT, REVEREND AMBROSE and JEFFERSON. OH!! *(They are all shocked.)*

MISS EMMA. AH!! *(She throws her arms around Jefferson.)* Forgive me, my boy! Oh, Jesus my Master? What I done, Master? *(Reverend Ambrose puts his arms around both Miss Emma and Jefferson.)*

REVEREND AMBROSE. Now, now. Now, then.

MISS EMMA. What I done done, my Master?

REVEREND AMBROSE. Hush, now. Trust in God.

MISS EMMA. Jefferson, my boy? What I done done, to make my Master hate me so?

REVEREND AMBROSE. God is only testing you. Testing you both. God be with you! *(Jefferson jerks himself back away from them.)*

JEFFERSON. *(To Grant.)* Damn this!

GRANT. Jefferson!

JEFFERSON. They go'n fry me in that 'lektric cher! I got to listen to this?

REVEREND AMBROSE. That is no way to talk!

JEFFERSON. They ain't frying *you!*

MISS EMMA. That's the preacher, Jefferson!

JEFFERSON. I don't care! Get out! All y'all! LEAVE ME ALONE!! *(The door opens. Enter Sheriff Guidry and Paul Bonin. Guidry grabs Jefferson and throws him against the wall.)*

SHERIFF GUIDRY. You can be heard all over town! This foolishness is over! Everybody out! *(Blackout. Light up on the table at the Rainbow Club. Vivian is sitting at the table. She has a bag by her chair marked Edwin's. As before, she is grading papers. Enter Grant, with two double brandies and sodas.)*

GRANT. That sale at Edwin's on clothes now?

VIVIAN. No, just radios. But I had to get things for the children.

GRANT. Well, good.

VIVIAN. How are you?

GRANT. Wonderful!

VIVIAN. Grant?

GRANT. Never again!

VIVIAN. Never again what?

GRANT. That Courthouse! Not me!

VIVIAN. Grant.

GRANT. God *damn* it!

VIVIAN. Sit down, Grant, and don't talk to me like that.

GRANT. I've just been in that hellhole with Jefferson and Miss Emma *and* Reverend Ambrose! That's why I got brandy and sodas. Doubles!

VIVIAN. Thank you. Drink slowly.

GRANT. Cheers.

VIVIAN. Cheers. *(They sip their drinks, carefully.)* That better?

GRANT. Some. *(Pause.)*

VIVIAN. Enjoy it. Because you know you have to go back there.

GRANT. Why? So white men can search my body like I'm a criminal? Not the teacher I am but the nigger they want me to be? And Jefferson! He wants me feeling guilty, just like he wants Miss Emma feeling guilty and you feeling guilty and all of Louisiana feeling guilty, and who can blame him? But I'm not feeling guilty because I'm not! I didn't put him there! I do everything I know to keep people from going there! He's not going to make me like that, because I'm not going back there!

VIVIAN. Then what about me?

GRANT. What does any of it have to do with you?

VIVIAN. Everything. I have been through a bad marriage with a hard man. He hated me leaving him, and his mother is crazy to call me names and take our children. Now I have just about won my freedom. Soon as I get it, I am about to give it to you.

GRANT. You will never regret that.

VIVIAN. If I marry another man like him, yes, I will. I got to be sure of you.

GRANT. And you're not?

VIVIAN. Frankly, not entirely.

GRANT. I am a decent man!

VIVIAN. Decent men back out. Decent men make excuses. Decent men say one thing and do another. Decent men change the rules. Then decent men don't show up.

GRANT. I will give you everything I have, all my life. But don't ask me to go back there for the same damn thing over and over again! I can't do it!

VIVIAN. This is hard. But when Jefferson dies, I'm still a school-teacher. So are you. Children are our responsibility. Not only those we teach. Not only those we raise. But every child we taught in the past, like Jefferson.

GRANT. I'm responsible for Jefferson?

VIVIAN. If you aren't, you are running away. You have to stand up like a man, too.

GRANT. Not now I don't! The Sheriff says no more visits!

VIVIAN. Find a way.

GRANT. The Sheriff is a son of a bitch but he's right!

VIVIAN. He's wrong! Stop swearing and try again!

GRANT. I can't walk through iron bars. All Jefferson wants is to be left alone. I don't blame him! He wants to be a hog, let him be a hog! *(Pause.)*

VIVIAN. All right. Let's calm down, and think this through. Jefferson is young, and terrified. He's lived all his life dirt poor in the country, with kerosene lamps and fireplace heat. Been to town a dozen times in his life? Ever been in a courtroom before? How could he understand what goes on there? He has to be confused. Does Jefferson really understand what happened to him?

GRANT. Of course!

VIVIAN. I mean what he did and didn't do, exactly? Do you think he killed Mr. Gropé?

GRANT. I don't know. *(Thinks.)* No, I don't.

VIVIAN. But he was right there, half drunk, with stolen money in his hand, yes?

GRANT. Yes.

VIVIAN. He did commit crimes.

GRANT. No, not murder.

VIVIAN. Then think a minute. Two white men and a Deputy Sheriff walk in on an ignorant, innocent boy and he's arrested. He's on trial for murder. He's found guilty. He's going to die. Yes?

24

GRANT. Yes.

VIVIAN. His lawyer says hog. Miss Emma makes this federal case out of it and says be a man. That's a lot for a boy to live with, alone in a death cell. So he takes refuge in hating us and himself.

GRANT. That's right, but what can I do about it?

VIVIAN. Start by going over it. With him. What really happened to him. Do that much. Just — try.

GRANT. I'll ask the Sheriff. One more time, I'll try.

VIVIAN. Good for you. Cheers. *(They sip their drinks, and relax.)*

GRANT. So, how was Edwin's?

VIVIAN. As usual. Same sale on radios to get you there, then noting else.

GRANT. Oh, yeah. Radios.

VIVIAN. Little Philcos.

GRANT. How much?

VIVIAN. Ten dollars. *(Pause.)*

GRANT. Oh. Er, uh. Vivian.

VIVIAN. What?

GRANT. A radio. Bet he never had one of his own.

VIVIAN. Oh.

GRANT. I might get it to him somehow. You say ten?

VIVIAN. Yes, Grant. Here's two, from me. *(Vivian puts one, then two dollars on the table.)*

GRANT. Thanks. *(They smile at each other and sip. Lights down. Lights up on the bench at center. Enter Paul. Enter Grant. Grant carries a package marked Edwin's.)*

PAUL. Before we go in, there are these conditions. Limited visits, to be approved by me one at a time. Two day advance notice until seven days before the execution. And I have to stay in the room.

GRANT. How did it happen?

PAUL. Sheriff Guidry reconsidered your request.

GRANT. Why?

PAUL. His reelection.

GRANT. You point that out to him?

PAUL. He saw it himself.

GRANT. I think you did. Thank you.

PAUL. We might as well call each other by our names. Mine's Paul.

GRANT. Grant.

PAUL. Grant, listen here to me. I can't get too close to him.

GRANT. Okay.

PAUL. We're told keep your distance from somebody being executed. Be decent, treat him right, but that's all. Nobody's been executed in this Parish in fifty years. Everybody's nervous, and it'll get harder, before it's over.

GRANT. I know that.

PAUL. What are you bringing in?

GRANT. Same food. Few clean clothes. And this. *(He holds up the package marked Edwin's.)* It's a little radio. Can he have that in his cell?

PAUL. I'll have to ask but I don't see why not, he plays it low.

GRANT. You better inspect it.

PAUL. I been to Edwin's. I seen that radio. Go on in.

GRANT. Why are you helping out?

PAUL. That what you think I'm doing?

GRANT. Yes.

PAUL. I'm doing my duty.

GRANT. More than that.

PAUL. I don't think he did it.

GRANT. Why not? He could have.

PAUL. When I got called to that store, Jefferson was flustered, hot, in a panic. The way I'd be, I knew I looked guilty, and wasn't. Guilty people know better and stay cold. He even forgot to say he didn't do it. *(Exit Paul. Lights out on Grant. Lights up on Jefferson, in his usual handcuffs and leg chains, in the storeroom. Enter Grant, in darkness. Lights up on them. Paul, in the dim background, sits holding a folder, thick with onion skin carbons. He hands it to Grant.)*

GRANT. Pay attention, Jefferson. This is the transcript of the trial. That's what everybody said, all written down. I read it so I've been there now. I want you to go back over it with me. You do that?

JEFFERSON. Ain't deaf.

GRANT. Your lawyer said you were not guilty of murder. You were about to meet a friend named Gable at the White Rabbit Bar and Lounge when you ran into two men, nicknamed Brother and Bear. They had a car. Drove it up beside you. Said get in. Said come on with them to Mr. Gropé's and the three of you'd get some good Apple White. That what your lawyer said?

JEFFERSON. Maybe.

GRANT. Jefferson, we got to understand why you are here. I don't think you do, and I'm not positive I do either. Let's figure it out. In plain words we both understand. Can I go ahead?

JEFFERSON. Yeah.

GRANT. What your lawyer said then, based on confusing statements from you, was you and Brother and Bear went into Mr. Gropé's store. Yes?

JEFFERSON. I told him that.

GRANT. All right. Nobody there but the old man, Gropé. He saw you, asked about your Nanann, nice like. How she was. Brother and Bear wanted the Apple White. You remember this, Jefferson?

JEFFERSON. Don't want to remember it! Hurts too much!

GRANT. I know but come on. I need to see this. Brother and Bear didn't have more than pocket change. Mr. Gropé said not enough. They started around the counter. He pulled a pistol from under his cash register and then what? Jefferson, then what?

JEFFERSON. Mr. Gropé say, "Go back."

GRANT. Did they?

JEFFERSON. No.

GRANT. Did they stop?

JEFFERSON. No. Brother had a gun, too.

GRANT. Who shot who first?

JEFFERSON. Not sure.

GRANT. See, Jefferson, this is where it breaks down. That white jury didn't think you were telling the truth, even if you were. You hear me?

JEFFERSON. Yes!!

GRANT. Who shot first!

JEFFERSON. Don't know!

GRANT. Yes, you do! You keeping this all mixed up! Come on!!

JEFFERSON. Gropé!

GRANT. Did you tell your lawyer that?

JEFFERSON. No!

GRANT. Why not?

JEFFERSON. Say the white man shot first? I ain't no fool!

GRANT. Yes, you are, Jefferson, if you didn't tell the truth under oath! Instead, you lied and said you didn't know. Truth is, Gropé

27

shot Bear. Then Gropé shot Brother at the same time Brother shot Gropé. Brother's gun on the floor at your feet, and three men dead!

JEFFERSON. No, they wasn't.

GRANT. What?

JEFFERSON. Gropé was still alive. He talked to me.

GRANT. That's not in the transcript!

JEFFERSON. I never told it. He say, "Boy, boy, boy," over and over.

GRANT. What did you do?

JEFFERSON. I say, "Mr. Gropé, it wasn't me. It wasn't me." He say, "Boy," again and he looked off, at the wall. Then he died. Now they say I done it.

GRANT. You were alone. Only living man in the place.

JEFFERSON. Yes.

GRANT. Call the police? You could have.

JEFFERSON. I don't know how to use no telephone. Never even talked in one. I didn't know what to do. Stay or run? I needed a drink bad and I broke open that bottle of Apple White and drank half of it down. It made me crazy to get out of there, but I didn't have no money. Cash register was open. I grabbed some and white men walked in the door.

GRANT. Thank you, Jefferson. That's good, clear plain English. Now your lawyer said something for you, remember? He said the fact that Mr. Gropé shot only Brother and Bear and not at you was proof of your innocence. Why did he shoot at them and never at you? Come on. Why?

JEFFERSON. I was just there.

GRANT. Where you shouldn't have been. You should have gone with your friend Gable to the White Rabbit.

JEFFERSON. Wisht I had.

GRANT. What did that lawyer say you were before he called you a hog?

JEFFERSON. By stander.

GRANT. Innocent bystander, in the transcript. So, were you?

JEFFERSON. Yes. 'Cept — 'cept —

GRANT. Come on.

JEFFERSON. I was wrong to be there.

GRANT. Yes! That's right. You understand that?

JEFFERSON. Yes! What difference do it make?

28

GRANT. It is the difference between admitting what happened to you and denying it. You did wrong things. All right. I know what happened now. Your white lawyer saw that white jury did not believe your story, or his defense. They believed you were trying to lie your way out of robbery and murder. So he did something that just came naturally to him. He called you a hog. He used contempt for black people to try to get you off. He was a helpless, stupid white lawyer. He never meant you're a hog.

JEFFERSON. What he said.

GRANT. Yes, but now *you're* saying it and *you're* using it. And somewhere deep in you, you believe it! You shouldn't have been there. You lied about Gropé. When three men were dead, you stuffed money in your pocket and had yourself a big drink. And when that prosecutor nailed it down, what kind of animal you really are, drinking liquor over dead bodies, you thought, all right, that's what I'll be.

JEFFERSON. What you say.

GRANT. And then? Guess what? Then the blood of six generations of white men could not admit you were innocent, when you obviously very likely were. You could not stay alive when a white man lay dead. That jury was wrong. Bear and Brother were wrong. Gropé was wrong, pulling that gun. And you were wrong because you shouldn't have been there, *but that's all!* That's ALL you did! You were at the wrong place, at the wrong time. Face the truth, and walk like a man.

JEFFERSON. A man?

GRANT. Yes.

JEFFERSON. Who stands right up and walks to that cher?

GRANT. Yes.

JEFFERSON. You'd like that?

GRANT. Yes.

JEFFERSON. Me dead like that.

GRANT. I don't *want* you dead, Jefferson.

JEFFERSON. Then why you vex me?

GRANT. What?

JEFFERSON. How you like it, I vex you!

GRANT. Jefferson, what's this now?

JEFFERSON. How about that old yellow pussy you got!

29

GRANT. Jefferson.

JEFFERSON. Vex me, I vex you!

GRANT. You talking about Vivian Baptiste?

JEFFERSON. That old pussy ain't no good. Everybody had it. Husband, you, everybody else. Why you like worn out yellow pussy, Mr. Teacher?

GRANT. Vivian Baptiste, Jefferson, is the only reason I am still here trying to help you. Without her, I would have told you to go to hell a long time ago.

JEFFERSON. 'At's right! And then go!

GRANT. What?

JEFFERSON. Detroit! Chicago! That's where you going, ain't it?

GRANT. I might.

JEFFERSON. You sho ain't staying here with the likes of me!

GRANT. Maybe not!

JEFFERSON. Why should you? I see it. You can't stand looking at me! I am what you want to get away from! Why don't you say it? You can't stand the sight of me!

GRANT. No, Jefferson.

JEFFERSON. Me, the whole fourth grade, none of us! You can't look at none of us!! *(A very long pause. Grant finally nods.)*

GRANT. You're right, Jefferson. You're being honest and I'm not. It is hard to look at you. And at my students. And I do want to leave you.

JEFFERSON. Because you hate us?

GRANT. Because I get tired, thinking one big vicious circle.

JEFFERSON. What?

GRANT. The same thing, happening over and over. I think you, Bill, Jerry, Claudee, Smitty, Snowball. You remember Snowball.

JEFFERSON. Yeah.

GRANT. And the others, all gone. I hear the news, coming back. Somebody dead, somebody sent to prison for killing somebody else. Snowball was stabbed to death in a nightclub in Port Allen. You didn't know that?

JEFFERSON. No.

GRANT. Claudee got shot by a woman in New Orleans. Smitty, state penitentiary for manslaughter. Others who just died slower. So what's the use?

JEFFERSON. You 'posed to tell me.

GRANT. I'm trying.

JEFFERSON. You ain't very good at it. Huh? Who your teacher?

GRANT. What?

JEFFERSON. You was mine. Who was yours?

GRANT. My teacher, Jefferson, was a man from New Orleans. His name was Matthew Antoine, and he was as white as Sheriff Guidry. He could have passed, lived anywhere, easy, but he would-n't. He taught me, all right. He taught me bitterness. He said most of us would die in violence. Those who didn't white men would turn into animals, to escape it. Animals. "You'll see," he said. "Run! I wish I had." He was honest, but a terrible teacher. He had contempt for himself and contempt for us. He hated us for being black and he hated himself for looking white. That kind of bitter-ness is what Vivian Baptiste won't have, and because of her, I won't have it either. I am trying to keep you from that, at least.

JEFFERSON. Sho. You and your yellow pussy wants Jefferson to have good manners when he dies.

GRANT. *What?*

JEFFERSON. That's for the living. Jefferson is dead meat.

GRANT. Jefferson, for God's sake!

JEFFERSON. You and your damn woman go on and live. But I swear, that old Mr. Antoine sounds like he knowed more than you do! Maybe I should had him for my teacher and not her and not you! Aw, go away from me! I can't do this no more!

PAUL. Grant.

GRANT. Yes.

PAUL. He said no more.

GRANT. Can he keep the radio?

PAUL. I'll take it to his cell with him. But Grant, and you too, Jefferson. Before we leave, there's something I got to do and you have to help me. Sheriff turned it over to me.

GRANT. Yes?

PAUL. Be a witness.

GRANT. What do I do?

PAUL. Just stand there. *(Paul takes a piece of paper from his folder.)* The warrant came down from the Governor today. I have to read part of it to you, Jefferson. Stand there, please. *(Jefferson does. Paul*

31

reads aloud.) "The Supreme Court of Louisiana has affirmed the death penalty in this case. In accordance of Act Number Fourteen of 1940, the sheriff of St. Raphael Parish is ordered to cause the electrocution of the condemned person within the walls of the St. Raphael Parish Courthouse in the manner provided by law, on April eighth, 1948, between the hours of twelve o'clock P.M. and three o'clock P.M. Signed by the Governor. Please say you heard that.

JEFFERSON. I heard it.

PAUL. Grant? The same.

GRANT. I heard it, Paul.

PAUL. Thank you.

JEFFERSON. That how long?

PAUL. Five weeks. And five days. *(Pause. Paul opens the door for Grant.)*

JEFFERSON. You say radio?

PAUL. Mr. Wiggins brought you one.

GRANT. I haven't helped you. Maybe it can. *(Paul unwraps the radio and holds it up.)*

PAUL. It runs on batteries. Here. *(Paul gives the radio to Jefferson. Jefferson just holds it and looks at it. Paul shows him a knob.)* Turn it on. *(Jefferson turns on the radio. It plays static. He twists the dial and good music plays. The three men stand listening to it. Slowly, gravely, Jefferson nods in time to the music. Paul and Grant look at each other. Paul folds the death warrant and holds it behind his back. They listen to the good music. Grant starts to leave.)*

JEFFERSON. Mr. Wiggins.

GRANT. Yes?

JEFFERSON. You be back?

GRANT. I'll be back. *(Exit Grant. Jefferson stands holding his radio, playing music as the lights fade.)*

End of Act One

ACT TWO

Lights come up on the Rainbow Club, where Vivian is wetting one end of a handkerchief in a glass of water. Grant sits by her as she soaks a lump on his forehead, not very gently.

GRANT. Don't be mad at me.

VIVIAN. I'm not mad, I'm disgusted.

GRANT. I was happy! Jefferson said, "Come back." I got to him, for the first time. I was feeling good, for the first time. Then this happened. Look, I had to do it.

VIVIAN. Who were they?

GRANT. Bricklayers.

VIVIAN. You couldn't fight another schoolteacher?

GRANT. Mulattos, who don't work in the field, and try to act white. They saw me in the drugstore. Started talking loud. One said, "Should have burned him months ago." Other said, "That kind of nigger makes it hard on all of us." First one said, "I'd pull that switch myself." I said, "Shut up," and hit him before he could hit me.

VIVIAN. Thank you. A vulgar brawl in a public place. Thank you.

GRANT. I didn't start it.

VIVIAN. You were ready. You were more than ready.

GRANT. What if I was? What the hell. Twelve white men say a black man must die. Another white man sets the date and time without consulting one black person. No proof the defendant had anything to do with the crime other than being there when it happened. Should be thrown out of court. Instead, white folks set a date convenient to them, not too close to Easter! An old woman wants me to stop what's been going on for three hundred years. A preacher tells me I'm sending a soul to hell. My pathetic excuse for a school turns me into a drill master for robots, and two other black men want to electrocute Jefferson themselves. What's going to change?

33

VIVIAN. You. Grant, Miss Emma is not the fool you think she is. When a black child is promising, like you were, like I was, we get put through school. Why? Not just to read books. To teach what that old lady really wants taught. And what is that? To be able, someday, to stand up to the white man. *For her!* That's the real reason she wants Jefferson to walk to that chair. Because if he doesn't, she will never live to see a black man stand up for her, or me, or any woman. That's what that old lady you think is a fool wants. Men, standing up for her.

GRANT. I just stood up for Jefferson!

VIVIAN. Fist fighting is not standing up for anybody.

GRANT. Suppose someone said something about you? Expect me to do nothing?

VIVIAN. Yes.

GRANT. I couldn't!

VIVIAN. Then one day I bring flowers to the graveyard.

GRANT. Don't talk like that.

VIVIAN. Then like what? Talk how? Tell me how?

GRANT. All I know is I love you.

VIVIAN. That's what you say when you're losing out. What's love, Grant?

GRANT. Vivian honey —

VIVIAN. The bed? That's love? Because if it is, we're not doing so good lately. Every time you go near that Courthouse, it's not so good in that bed.

GRANT. I know that and I'm sorry. Nothing is worth us not happy in bed.

VIVIAN. Yes, Grant some things are! That's what I'm trying to tell you! There are other things to be considered!

GRANT. Vivian, please —

VIVIAN. No, give me some answers!

GRANT. I love you.

VIVIAN. That's no answer. Love like in a bed? A double brandy? Baton Rouge. A brawl in a store?

GRANT. God damn this!

VIVIAN. Say goodbye again? Take the easy way out?

GRANT. What the hell do you want from me?

VIVIAN. Run away?

GRANT. No! I'm doing my best!

VIVIAN. You are not! There is more!

GRANT. Like what?

VIVIAN. Seeing something through!

GRANT. Stop it!

VIVIAN. Not running away!

GRANT. I said, stop it!

VIVIAN. Staying where you belong! *(Grant jumps up.)*

GRANT. Damn this shit! Get yourself a superman! Get yourself a white man!

VIVIAN. No, I got myself a black coward! How can you ask a boy to face an electric chair when you won't face yourself?

GRANT. You say that to me?

VIVIAN. Easy as pie! Run away, go ahead! He can't! So you are both wronged by the white man. I know that. We all are. What does it change? Nothing. What changes things, is you and me staying here and teaching the children. Teaching you say is for nothing! Some of it is, but not all! Not every life gets lost! And if we don't do this, what about you and your life? What about me and my life? What about our life! Answer me!

GRANT. I can't!! *(Vivian jumps up.)*

VIVIAN. Then goodbye!

GRANT. Goodbye! *(A terrible pause.)*

VIVIAN. This is wrecking us. *(They both sit down again.)* We should do this together. I should do my part and not just blame you. I have to do something, too. *(Lights down on the Rainbow Club. Morning light up on the schoolroom. Grant enters with papers to grade. He puts some old sacks and bags at one end of the desk, all empty. He begins grading. It is slow work and he must mark almost every sentence. Enter Reverend Ambrose. He watches Grant for a moment, unseen. Then he steps into the classroom, smiling.)*

REVEREND AMBROSE. Good morning.

GRANT. Good morning. *(Grant stands up.)* Reverend, the children don't get here for another hour.

REVEREND AMBROSE. Sacks and bags? What are they for?

GRANT. The children want to take some pecans to Jefferson. Would you like to sit down? *(Reverend Ambrose sits in Grant's chair.)*

REVEREND AMBROSE. I understand the date is set.

GRANT. Friday after Easter.

REVEREND AMBROSE. Three weeks.

GRANT. Twenty days.

REVEREND AMBROSE. He ain't saved.

GRANT. I can't help you there.

REVEREND AMBROSE. And why can't you? Because you educated?

GRANT. I teach reading, writing, and arithmetic. You save souls.

REVEREND AMBROSE. Well, he don't need no more 'rithmetic. When you going back?

GRANT. Next week.

REVEREND AMBROSE. What you go'n talk about?

GRANT. I don't know.

REVEREND AMBROSE. I'm going tomorrow. I'm go'n talk about God.

GRANT. Jefferson needs to hear it.

REVEREND AMBROSE. He needs to hear there is a better world than this one, and believe it. But I need your help. He listens to you more than me.

GRANT. I'm sorry. I don't believe in that other world.

REVEREND AMBROSE. Meaning you educated. Son, you don't know nothing. I'm the one that's educated. By life and by death. But you, you look down on me. Just a preacher. Just a liar. What do I preach? You say fairy tales and lies. If so, I tell lies to relieve pain. I preach to people in pain. Oh Pain, when will you stop! When the children of man have grief and sorrow in the awful pain of this life, where is hope? None, there is none, 'til God speaks. And God says there *is* hope, there is blessed release from pain and grief, across yon river, and some of us believe! To relieve that pain! Do you hear what I trying to say to you, boy?

GRANT. Reverend, save Jefferson's soul! I'm not in your way!

REVEREND AMBROSE. Yes, you are!

GRANT. You're mad because Miss Emma brought me into it and you're jealous! I wish to God she hadn't and you weren't! But what do you want me to do about it?

REVEREND AMBROSE. First time you say God, you insult me. You got no time for a preacher, or the Bible. But your fine education is not enough. Life is harder than that. Why? Because people got pain! You don't give 'em rithmetic! Look what pain done for you! Your Aunt Lou, Miss Emma, and others, hands bleeding from picking cotton, scabs on their knees scrubbing floors, putting dollars one at time in a jar, to send a boy, *you,* to college! Why? To come back and *stop* the pain! Her pain! And what you do, Teacher? Nothing! Jefferson will die, not saved, and she will die, in that pain! Because you are not helping nothing!

GRANT. I am killing myself just staying here!

REVEREND AMBROSE. Maybe you shouldn't! What kind of teacher were you for this boy? Why he never finish even the fourth grade?

GRANT. He couldn't! He didn't want to! How do I know?

REVEREND AMBROSE. Because what you taught him was ungodly! It was wrong and it was bad! As *you* are!

GRANT. I am doing the best I can, on this damn battlefield where we fight over a boy who'll be dead in three weeks! What for? Just leave him alone!

REVEREND AMBROSE. And let his soul, his immortal soul, die? Never!

GRANT. Then we are no better than that white lawyer! Miss Emma tells him eat her food and act right. You tell him pray to God and go to heaven. I tell him face death and be a man. We might as well tell him be a hog. What's the difference?

REVEREND AMBROSE. You are a fool. God have mercy on you, boy.

GRANT. I hear boy from white men, Reverend. Please. I don't want to hear it from you. *(There is a deadly pause. The Reverend Ambrose stalks out of the room. Lights down on the schoolroom. Lights up on storeroom. Paul is waiting for Grant. He paces back and forth, unhappy. Enter Grant. He carries a paper sack. Paul speaks to someone in the outside corridor.)*

PAUL. You wait here. *(Paul and Grant face each other in the storeroom.)* Grant.

GRANT. Paul.

PAUL. Fistfight? You can't do that.

GRANT. I know it.

PAUL. I half convinced the sheriff it wasn't your fault, but I think it was.

GRANT. Maybe so.

PAUL. We are getting too close to this. You hit some bastard in a store, I can't let you see him anymore! You hear?

GRANT. No more fights.

PAUL. What's in the sack?

GRANT. Comic books. Apples and candy bars. A little notebook and a pencil.

PAUL. Let me see. *(Grant empties the contents of the sack.)* How can I trust you? Want to hit Guidry? Want to hit me?

GRANT. Yes. But I won't.

PAUL. Okay.

GRANT. Okay.

PAUL. Oh, the children sent pecans. He ate some. He likes the radio. *(Exit Paul, down the corridor. Grant takes comic books out of the paper sack, looks at them, puts them back. He takes the small notebook from his pocket, with a pencil and a small pencil sharpener. He stares at them all bleakly. Grant takes one of the old benches and sits down on one end of it. He puts his notebook on the bench with the pencil and the sharpener. He almost breaks down. He hears them coming. He puts the notebook and the pencil and the sharpener back in his pocket. Paul and Jefferson come down the corridor. Grant stands up and makes himself smile.)* One hour.

JEFFERSON. Mr. Paul?

PAUL. Yes?

JEFFERSON. How long is it from now?

PAUL. Twelve days.

JEFFERSON. What day it go'n be?

PAUL. Friday.

JEFFERSON. Close to Easter?

PAUL. Just after.

JEFFERSON. 'Bout springtime.

PAUL. Yeah. *(Paul sits in the background.)*

GRANT. Jefferson. Got you some apples and a couple candy bars. Some funny books. *(Grant hands Jefferson the paper sack.)* Want an apple?

JEFFERSON. No. Don't you get a big meal before you die?

GRANT. I think so.

JEFFERSON. Mr. Paul?

PAUL. Whatever you want.

JEFFERSON. I want me a whole gallon ice cream, not no apple. Vanilla. Eat it with a pot spoon. Never had more than a nickel cone. Now I'll get a whole gallon.

GRANT. I can bring you ice cream anytime, Jefferson.

JEFFERSON. I'm go'n wait. Whole gallon. Eat it with a pot spoon.

GRANT. Like your radio?

JEFFERSON. It's all right.

GRANT. Can you get Randy's Record Shop on it?

JEFFERSON. Yeah. And I get Del Rio, Texas and even Nashville. How'd you get a Philco?

GRANT. I asked people to help me.

JEFFERSON. Who?

GRANT. Miss Vivian. She gave me two dollars and the idea in the first place.

JEFFERSON. Oh.

GRANT. Claiborne, runs the Rainbow Club, he gave me one.

JEFFERSON. Why?

GRANT. He knows music is important, and he wanted you to have it. That made three. We went up and down his bar two nights. Came up with three more. That was six. I did four and the sales tax.

JEFFERSON. Thank him for me.

GRANT. All right.

JEFFERSON. And thank you.

GRANT. You're welcome.

JEFFERSON. And thank her.

GRANT. Do that yourself. Paul? *(Grant opens the door. Vivian is standing there. She enters, lovely and smiling, in a flower print dress, bringing with her into the drab room all the freshness and beauty of spring. Jefferson is overwhelmed.)*

VIVIAN. Jefferson. Thank you for letting me come to see you. I have been wanting to for a long time. *(Jefferson stares at her, stricken.)* I've been thinking about you. Grant tells me all about it, how brave you are, how good and strong you are. Now I can see that for myself.

JEFFERSON. I — I —

VIVIAN. He says you are doing fine, and learning a lot and he's learning a lot. So I wanted to come here myself to tell you how much I care about you, and how much everybody in this town cares about you.

JEFFERSON. Oh.

VIVIAN. We are all thinking about you, Jefferson. All the time. God bless you. *(Vivian holds out her arms. Jefferson, stunned by her warmth, stumbles toward her. She embraces him, and kisses him on the cheek. She holds him close for a moment. then steps back and smiles at him.)* Now, I will let you men get on with your work. *(She goes to the door, and waves cheerfully.)* Jefferson.

JEFFERSON. Thank you coming to see me.

VIVIAN. You are welcome. *(Exit Vivian. Jefferson takes some time getting hold of himself.)*

JEFFERSON. Mr. Wiggins, I never meant what I said about her.

GRANT. I know that.

JEFFERSON. Nice lady, do that for me.

GRANT. She meant what she said.

JEFFERSON. And it was good of the chirens, bring me all them pecans.

GRANT. Here's something else if you want it. It's a notebook and a pencil, and, I forgot — *(Grant takes a pencil sharpener from his pocket.)* a pencil sharpener.

PAUL. I'll keep the sharpener. He can have the notebook and the pencil. *(Paul takes the sharpener.)*

GRANT. You may want to write things down. Anything, just write it down.

JEFFERSON. You know I never made it out of fourth grade. Can't spell.

GRANT. If you want to. *(Grant holds them out. Jefferson takes them.)* Do you talk to Reverend Ambrose?

JEFFERSON. He talks to me. All he tells me is pray.

GRANT. Do you?

JEFFERSON. No.

GRANT. Be good for your Nannan.

JEFFERSON. What for? You think I'm going to heaven?

GRANT. I don't know.

JEFFERSON. Then what do I pray for?

GRANT. For your Nannan.

JEFFERSON. She don't need me get to heaven. She'll make it, if it's up there.

GRANT. Well, she wants you up there with her.

JEFFERSON. You pray?

GRANT. No.

JEFFERSON. Then why should I?

GRANT. I don't know.

JEFFERSON. If you can't pray, how can I?

GRANT. I don't know. Look. I'm lost, Jefferson. I don't believe in anything. Not like your Nannan does. Not like the Reverend Ambrose does. But I want to. Maybe I want you to believe so one day I will.

JEFFERSON. In heaven, Mr. Wiggins?

GRANT. If it helps people on earth.

JEFFERSON. Reverend Ambrose say I got to give up what's on earth.

GRANT. He means possessions. Cars, money, clothes.

JEFFERSON. You ever seen me with a car?

GRANT. No.

JEFFERSON. With more than a dollar in my pocket?

GRANT. No.

JEFFERSON. Then what on earth I got to give up?

GRANT. Nothing. What I'm asking is for Miss Emma. She cooked for you, washed for you, nursed you when you were sick.

JEFFERSON. Now she want something.

GRANT. For you to walk like a man.

JEFFERSON. To the 'lektric cher? When I didn't do nothing to nobody. Like it's all right, like I don't care? That's what she wants?

GRANT. Well, yes.

JEFFERSON. That's asking a lot from a poor nigger never had nothing.

GRANT. She would do it for you.

JEFFERSON. She sit in that cher for me?

GRANT. Maybe.

JEFFERSON. You do it?

GRANT. No.

JEFFERSON. I got to go there myself.

GRANT. I wish I knew what to say, Jefferson.

JEFFERSON. I'm the one got to figure it out. My momma can't. My daddy can't. Left me, they did. Growed up going to the field at six in the morning. Ever since I can remember. Water cart. Cotton sack. Cussed at for nothing. Beat for nothing. Work for nothing. Was nothing. I'll write *that* down. When you going?

GRANT. What?

JEFFERSON. Detroit, Chicago. You told me you got to California once. You like it there?

GRANT. I'm glad I went.

JEFFERSON. Glad you come back?

GRANT. Not always.

JEFFERSON. You going to California again?

GRANT. I don't know.

JEFFERSON. You have a somebody like Nannan, too?

GRANT. So what's this? You asking the questions now?

JEFFERSON. She said talk.

GRANT. My Tante Lou was like your Miss Emma.

JEFFERSON. She brung you up, when your momma and daddy didn't, like my Nannan did me?

GRANT. Yes.

JEFFERSON. Both of us got left behind, huh?

GRANT. Yes.

JEFFERSON. You like that?

GRANT. I liked my Tante Lou. Not being left behind.

JEFFERSON. Won't be both of us for very long. Just you. When you go'n die, Mr. Teacher?

GRANT. I don't know when I'm going to die. Maybe tomorrow, maybe next week, maybe today.

JEFFERSON. Wish we was white?

GRANT. What's this now, Jefferson, you're doing to me?

JEFFERSON. Miss Emma said talk.

GRANT. No, I don't wish I was white.

JEFFERSON. Lot easier. Teach anywhere.

GRANT. I am who I am, Jefferson. I am like you, and I am glad I am like you.

JEFFERSON. So when you going to California? Who *you* leaving behind? See, I got to understand what I'm to do here. I

42

thought I did. Just be what the white man said. Let them drag the hog to the cher, damned if I'll walk for them. And I still don't know what I am go'n do! Walk or get dragged! Because — either way — ah, Mr. Paul!

PAUL. Okay, Jefferson. *(Paul and Jefferson go to the door.)*

JEFFERSON. This hard. Old Hog has to figure it out. *(Exit Jefferson, then Paul. Light fades on Grant. Light on the schoolroom. Enter Grant. He has a paper in his hand. He looks at the students from behind the table, then he comes around to the front of it.)*

GRANT. Jefferson thanks you for the pecans. I got your paper with all your names on it. I thank Odessa Freeman for writing it up in straight lines. It looks good. I took it to the Courthouse and per-mission has been granted. It will be arranged for all of you to say hello to Jefferson in the Day Room in person. I am very much impressed that you thought of this on your own. I have been hard on you in the past because I thought you needed that. But at this moment, you have nothing but my respect and my admiration. Two trucks will be ready tomorrow morning to take you to the jail and bring you back. We will have a brief recess and then geography, and I will be hard on you again. *(Lights fade on the classroom. Lights on the Reverend Ambrose, going to the bench. He sits. Grant goes to him.)*

REVEREND AMBROSE. First, a sin box. Now a notebook and pencil. All he does is listen to the radio and write in the notebook. Talk to me? Talk to Miss Emma? No! See what you done!

GRANT. Yes. I gave him a radio, and a pencil and notebook.

REVEREND AMBROSE. He should be praying to his God, not listening no radio, writing in no book —

GRANT. And I would do it again. Both are good for him.

REVEREND AMBROSE. You are sending his soul to hell.

GRANT. I want him in heaven as much as you do, Reverend.

REVEREND AMBROSE. Oh, how can that be, if it's a place you don't believe in?

GRANT. No, I don't believe in it.

REVEREND AMBROSE. Then how can you tell him believe in it?

GRANT. I will never tell him not to.

REVEREND AMBROSE. And that's all? Face eternity, with a pencil and a radio??

GRANT. It's the best I can do!

REVEREND AMBROSE. Suppose he write, "When I die, will heaven be there?" What you say then?

GRANT. I hope he doesn't ask me that.

REVEREND AMBROSE. Suppose he do!

GRANT. Then I won't lie to him!

REVEREND AMBROSE. Not for her sake? Not for his?

GRANT. No, sir. *(Reverend Ambrose stands up.)*

REVEREND AMBROSE. I'm taking that sin box away from him. I am breaking that pencil in two. I will burn that notebook! *(Grant stands up.)*

GRANT. If you do, I won't go in there again!

REVEREND AMBROSE. That would be the best thing that could happen to him. Sister Emma tells me you hate teaching. You hate the South. You going away, and not teaching our children any more. Well, good! *(Exit the Reverend Ambrose. Lights up on the storeroom. Paul sits in the background, reading a newspaper. Grant goes to the storeroom, and sits reading Jefferson's notebook, while Jefferson watches him.)*

JEFFERSON. You don't like it.

GRANT. *(Reading.)* Yes, I do.

JEFFERSON. It's spelled all wrong.

GRANT. Never mind the spelling. Just cross words out.

JEFFERSON. I did.

GRANT. I can read this. I like it.

JEFFERSON. What do you like?

GRANT. I like this bad dream.

JEFFERSON. Over and over. Walking to somewhere I don't know where, and 'fore I get to the door I wake up, so scared. I know that behind that door is the cher. You like that?

GRANT. Make you feel better now you wrote about it, or worse?

JEFFERSON. Better.

GRANT. What did you write about that doesn't feel better?

JEFFERSON. When Reven Ambrose ask me if I know the Lord died for me. Do I want to meet God and the angels in heavens with all my heart and soul? Nannan start crying again. Say, Lord forgive our sin. Her and Reven Ambrose praying and praying on their knees. I was glad when Paul said, time's up, and took me out of there.

GRANT. I see that here. You wrote, "About God. I just don't

44

understand." Good.

JEFFERSON. Not understanding is good?

GRANT. Knowing that you don't is.

JEFFERSON. What you like I wrote?

GRANT. What we see outside that window.

JEFFERSON. Just a tree. Birds. Some sky.

GRANT. You just put it down, what's there. Good. What's out there now?

JEFFERSON. Some bird.

GRANT. What kind of bird?

JEFFERSON. Like a bluebird.

GRANT. I see you wrote about the children.

JEFFERSON. Lord, yes!

GRANT. Why?

JEFFERSON. They come here, to see me. That whole class! Some scared to look at me, I could see that.

GRANT. And you set that down. Good.

JEFFERSON. But most was brave. My little cousin Estelle even come up and kiss me on the jaw. I couldn't hold it back no more and cried and then the next day it look like everybody from the quarter come here.

GRANT. And you took note of who did.

JEFFERSON. Well, sho, 'cause there was — *(Jefferson looks in the notebook with Grant.)* Miss Julia and Joe and Auntie Agnes and Miss Harriet and Mr. Newman and Miss Sara, Miss Lila, Mr. Harry, and Miss Lena, and little Bok and God knows who all.

GRANT. And when they left did you read what you wrote?

JEFFERSON. Yes, and remembered all kind of things. That suit half little Bok's size cause Miss Rita got it, I reckon, near two year ago. Now him still in it, arms sticking out, like this. *(They smile.)* Little Bok give me a marble. You know how he is, always looking all around all the time.

GRANT. Little Bok, a little off in the head.

JEFFERSON. Yeah. Well, he reach in his pocket and pull out a marble to give me, and it was his Agie. Best one. He didn't want to give me no big Agie! So he stuck it back in his pocket, and he pull out a little Pee Wee! *(Jefferson laughs. Grant smiles.)* He wanted to give me something, but not that Agie! A Pee Wee! *(They laugh at this together.)*

GRANT. And you saw that. And wrote it down.

JEFFERSON. And when Miss Vivian come to see me. And y'all look so good together. She got on a pretty dress with pretty flowers on it. She talk so nice to me, not putting on airs, just quality in her. Me so ugly but she smell so sweet and she say I'm looking good and strong. She put her hand right here on my shoulder. I start tremblin', and she lean close and kiss me. She was the first lady that pretty ever touch me. When she left, I could smell her powder scent and feel her mouth on my face.

GRANT. And you wrote that down, too.

JEFFERSON. Uh-huh. What grade you giving me for this work?

GRANT. B plus.

JEFFERSON. Not no A?

GRANT. Not yet.

JEFFERSON. What I got to do to get a A?

GRANT. A good man asked me to look deep in me. I couldn't then but I am trying to now. You do that, and write it down, what you feel deep in you.

JEFFERSON. Deep in me?

GRANT. Deep in you.

JEFFERSON. Well. Last time I seen Nannan, how old she look, how tired. Thought about her. Said I loves her. She never kiss me my whole life before but she did then. I let her hold me as long as she want. I'll write about that. So I don't forget. *(Jefferson writes in his notebook. He breaks the pencil point.)*

JEFFERSON. Broke the point.

PAUL. Here. *(Paul comes, takes the pencil and with the pencil sharpener he has kept in his pocket, he carefully sharpens Jefferson's pencil for him.)*

JEFFERSON. I'm go'n have Nannan cook me a pork chop for my last meal. With okra and rice and cornbread.

GRANT. What about all that ice cream?

JEFFERSON. Just a little Dixie cup, and a moon pie.

PAUL. Here. *(Paul hands Jefferson his pencil, sharpened.)* Let me know when you need it again.

JEFFERSON. Yes, sir. *(Paul goes back to his seat.)* I keep on looking, deep in me?

GRANT. Yes.

JEFFERSON. That'll make my writing better?

GRANT. It will. B plus is good work. That A can't be far off.

JEFFERSON. I'll get it. You tried hard, Mr. Wiggins. Make me think I'm somebody.

GRANT. You are somebody.

JEFFERSON. You look tired, too, Mr. Wiggins. Like Nannan. I'll write that down, too. And I'll write down, you a good man.

GRANT. So are you, Jefferson.

JEFFERSON. I never said that to nobody and nobody never said that to me.

GRANT. Now we have.

JEFFERSON. I'll write about it. *(Exit Jefferson, and then Paul. Lights down. Lights up on The Rainbow Club. Enter Vivian and Grant, drinks in their hands.)*

GRANT. It has to be done here.

VIVIAN. Why?

GRANT. It's in the warrant. It has to happen in the Parish where the crime was committed. No real prison in the Parish. That means the Courthouse.

VIVIAN. How can they do it?

GRANT. They have to truck in the chair tomorrow morning. Paul Bonin says they'll hide it, so people won't get upset. It will be in something marked "State Government," inside some crate or under some canvas. They carry the chair inside, then back the truck up to the window. Wires go from the generator on the back of the truck through the window to the chair.

VIVIAN. People can see that?

GRANT. And hear it. And they have to test it. It'll be heard blocks away.

VIVIAN. What?

GRANT. Things go wrong. Electricity gets interrupted, not be enough. So they make sure. Oh, yeah. With the chair, comes a real live State Executioner.

VIVIAN. Executioner?

GRANT. Some electrician, Paul said, who doesn't mind a job on the side. Sometimes they know what they're doing and sometimes they don't. Bodies catch on fire. Eyes blow out. Sometimes they have to do it twice, three times.

VIVIAN. Oh, Grant. Where in the Courthouse are they going to do it?

GRANT. In the only room big enough for the witnesses, and Jefferson, and the chair. The storeroom.

VIVIAN. Where you've been *meeting* him?

GRANT. Tomorrow, between twelve and three.

VIVIAN. Will you be there?

GRANT. No, I'll be at school. Reverend Ambrose will be there. I can't walk those last steps with Jefferson. He can.

VIVIAN. Miss Emma?

GRANT. She'll wait for Reverend Ambrose outside, to come tell her it's done. How about yourself?

VIVIAN. I'm staying home from school, with my children.

GRANT. Won't that get you in trouble?

VIVIAN. No colored people are working in town tomorrow.

GRANT. None on the plantation, either.

VIVIAN. Are you going to see Jefferson again?

GRANT. Once more this afternoon. *(Grant and Vivian hold hands tightly. Lights out on them as lights come up on the storeroom. Miss Emma and the Reverend Ambrose enter and set up a sort of table, from two storeroom boxes and a tablecloth Miss Emma has brought with her. There is a pan of gumbo, four spoons and four plates and paper napkins with four Coca-Colas on the box, like a picnic. Enter Grant. Reverend Ambrose turns away from him. Miss Emma nods. They wait. Enter Jefferson and Paul. Jefferson carries his radio in his arms, turned off. Paul sits further upstage, and watches them.)*

MISS EMMA. Well, Jefferson. We all here. We still don't know what you going to do, but we hope and pray for you, and we got you something good to eat. Will you listen if Reverend Ambrose prays for us, just a little while? *(Jefferson nods.)*

REVEREND AMBROSE. *(Praying.)* I simply ask you, Lord, come down into this town, come down into this Courthouse, and walk among us here. Go into each cell, touch each and every heart.

MISS EMMA. Yes, Lord.

REVEREND AMBROSE. Be with us is all we ask. Bless the gift on this table, to nourish our bodies so we may do thy will. Amen.

MISS EMMA and GRANT. Amen. *(Then three people speak at once.)*

REVEREND AMBROSE. *(Simultaneous.)* Now, you, you hear the Word of God!

MISS EMMA. *(Simultaneous.)* Jefferson, I hope you like my

JEFFERSON. *(Simultaneous.)* Can I play my radio? *(There terrible pause.)*

MISS EMMA. Oh, what we go'n do here?

REVEREND AMBROSE. Listen to the Bible, not a radio!

MISS EMMA. Lord, Lord, tell us what to do!

REVEREND AMBROSE. Maybe he knows!

MISS EMMA. Grant?

GRANT. I don't know what to do. Let's hope Jefferson does. *(Jefferson holds up the radio.)*

MISS EMMA. The radio, Jefferson?

JEFFERSON. Yes, ma'am.

REVEREND AMBROSE. Do you have to, now?

MISS EMMA. Let him.

REVEREND AMBROSE. Miss Emma!

MISS EMMA. Let him!

REVEREND AMBROSE. As you say. *(Jefferson turns on the radio. He finds a station playing something like "You are My Sunshine."*)*

MISS EMMA. Just turn it down a little. *(Jefferson turns it down.)* Like that.

REVEREND AMBROSE. Thank you. So? What now?

MISS EMMA. I called in the teacher. Grant. Teach.

REVEREND AMBROSE. And I have to listen to this?

MISS EMMA. For me!

REVEREND AMBROSE. For you. Well? Teacher? *(Grant goes and sits with Jefferson apart. Miss Emma and Reverend Ambrose don't look at them, but they listen. Grant speaks slowly and softly.)*

GRANT. Jefferson, do you know what a hero is? That is a man who does something for other people. Something other men can't do. I'm not a hero. Never will be. I want to run away. That is not a hero. A hero does for others. Like for your Nannan. Like for th children in the school. A hero would do anything for the peop he loves, to make their lives better. And a black hero has to f white people. Not all of them hate us, but a lot of them do. T

---

* See Special Note on Songs and Recordings on copyright page.

49

hink we are animals with no dignity, no heart, no love for our people. The last thing they want to see in a black man is the same good things that are in all men and all women. Look at me, Jefferson. *(Jefferson does.)* We need you, more than you need us. I am a man who doesn't know what to do. I need a hero to tell me what to do, and what kind of man to be. I need you, to teach me that. You can do that, for all of us, me, your Nannan, even Reverend Ambrose. You can be bigger and better than any man you or I have ever met. *(Enter, suddenly, Sheriff Guidry.)*

SHERIFF GUIDRY. *(Loud, cheerful.)* Folks, you'll have to move this along. Paul. *(Guidry summons Paul downstage for a conference. He strides about, pointing.)* We're getting a black curtain from the public school. It'll hang there, so we don't have to move all this stuff. The chair goes here, wired from the truck. Witnesses will come in — here, and stand here — and we'll bring him down the corridor between them. We got to get this ready pretty soon. *(He turns back and smiles at Jefferson.)* How're you, Jefferson?

JEFFERSON. All right.

SHERIFF GUIDRY. Anything you need?

JEFFERSON. Nossir.

SHERIFF GUIDRY. You been treated right here?

JEFFERSON. Yessir.

SHERIFF GUIDRY. We let these people visit you, and the children the other day. Play your radio. Keep your light on at night so you can write in your book?

JEFFERSON. Yessir.

SHERIFF GUIDRY. So you can write that down in there, too, right? *(Paul steps forward.)*

PAUL. A word with you, Sheriff. *(They step aside.)*

SHERIFF GUIDRY. Yes?

PAUL. *Please!*

SHERIFF GUIDRY. Oh. Yes. *(He looks at them all, at Miss Emma crying quietly, and realizes what he is doing.)* Everything will be — what it is. *(Sheriff Guidry goes to the door, stops.)* You folks take your time. *(Exit Sheriff Guidry.)*

PAUL. You heard him. *(Paul sits down again.)*

GRANT. Does anything I am saying mean anything to you?

JEFFERSON. You asking lots of me.

GRANT. That's what people do, of heroes.

JEFFERSON. Why can't a hero be dragged? Why walk, when it's wrong?

GRANT. I don't know the answer to that.

JEFFERSON. And you the teacher. You believe in God, like Reverend Ambrose?

GRANT. No. But you have made me think something makes people care about other people. I do believe that, now.

JEFFERSON. Reverend Ambrose says I have to give all that up, down here. Just God in heaven important now.

GRANT. Reverend Ambrose is a wise man.

JEFFERSON. But you been telling me something else, not that. You been telling me I'm the one. I got to do everything.

GRANT. I guess I have.

JEFFERSON. How?

GRANT. I don't know how. I just know you can.

JEFFERSON. You do?

GRANT. I do.

JEFFERSON. In one day? That's all I got. How I go'n do that? *(Jefferson stands up now, straight in his chains.)*

GRANT. You will know what to do. Because you're a better man than I am.

JEFFERSON. It make me a better man, 'cause I'm got to die tomorrow?

GRANT. I am having a hard time looking at you, Jefferson. I'm about to fall apart.

JEFFERSON. Well, don't. Do something else.

GRANT. What?

JEFFERSON. Stay here. Teach.

GRANT. Teach?

JEFFERSON. Yeah. Nannan? Reverend Ambrose?

MISS EMMA. Yes, Lord.

REVEREND AMBROSE. I agree he should. Yes, Lord.

JEFFERSON. Well?

GRANT. I promise — all of you that. *(Jefferson goes toward the window, looks out of it for a moment, then turns back to Grant.)*

JEFFERSON. In that 'lectric cher. What it go'n be like, Mr. Wiggins?

51

GRANT. It won't take long, Jefferson.

JEFFERSON. How you know?

GRANT. Read it in a book. Supposed to just knock you out.

JEFFERSON. Like Joe Louis?

GRANT. Yes, like Joe Louis.

JEFFERSON. I'm all right now. Let's go back and eat. *(Jefferson goes to the table.)* Preacher Ambrose. You sit here? *(Reverend Ambrose nods and stands at the chair Jefferson has indicated.)* Mr. Wiggins? *(Grant stands by the chair Jefferson indicates.)* Nannan. *(Miss Emma stand by the chair Jefferson indicates.)* Can you say the blessing again?

REVEREND AMBROSE. Bless this food, and the four of us, and thank you, Lord. Amen.

JEFFERSON. That gumbo sure smells good. Nannan, will you give mine to me?

MISS EMMA. Yes, my boy. *(Reverend Ambrose turns up the music on the radio. They sit down together. Lights fade slowly on Miss Emma serving them. We hear the voices of the schoolchildren.)*

CHILDREN'S VOICES. I pledge allegiance to the flag of the United States of America, and to the Republic for which it stands. One nation, indivisible, with liberty and justice for all. *(Grant moves to the classroom, stands speaking to his students.)*

GRANT. At twelve o'clock, we will stop our work, and you will be excused from class. If it is raining you will stay in the classroom, but if it is not, you will go outside on the grass under the trees. Please sit down there and wait. You can use handkerchiefs or coats if you wish to kneel. If you need to pray, do, but quietly, to yourselves. Please do not say anything to each other. Please think about Jefferson. When it is time, I will let you know. You will come back to class and I will tell you what has happened. *(As Grant speaks, the music fades and we hear the awful jump and hum of the crude generator. A black curtain descends on the back half of the storeroom. A bright light begins to appear at the center of the now empty room. Rising up from the floor, or sliding onstage, comes the terrible, strange, stark wooden structure of the electric chair, without much wiring but with its slab back slats, and its strange headrest. It is solid oak, worn but varnished, sturdy and awful. The buzzing noise from the generator gets louder and louder. The light falling on the empty chair gets brighter and brighter. The generator noise becomes very loud, then suddenly both stop. Light on the schoolroom. Grant sits at the desk. Paul enters the schoolroom.)*

PAUL. He died at one thirty-seven. He was the bravest man in the room. He said goodbye to me. He wished me well. Left me his radio. He wished Sheriff Guidry well. He thanked Reverend Ambrose. Any last words, he said, "Tell Nannan I walked." The state executioner strapped him in. Reverend Ambrose prayed one last time and did it well. The Executioner put a black cloth over his head. He took a deep breath, and we killed him. Here's his notebook. Some day I hope you will give me the privilege of reading it. *(Grant takes the notebook.)*

GRANT. Someday.

PAUL. Grant. I will never forget this day, or him, or you. Tell the children he was the bravest man in the room. I'm his witness.

GRANT. Maybe you'll come back and tell them yourself.

PAUL. It would be an honor. *(Exit Paul. Grant holds out his arms.)*

GRANT. Children, come in. I have things to tell you. *(Lights fade to half on Grant, waiting for the schoolchildren to come in. Music. Light comes up on the corridor, leading to the platform and the electric chair. Enter Jefferson, walking slowly but firmly through the corridor to the storeroom, alone. Jefferson wears a simple dark denim shirt and trousers, clean and pressed. He walks into the storeroom, stands by the chair. Light on his face and on Grant's, who is reading Jefferson's notebook. Music ends.)*

JEFFERSON. I don't know if you'll be able to read this, Mr. Wiggins. I can hear my heart beat and my hands shake. But I see the sun coming up in the morning. There is a bird in the sycamore tree. A bluebird. I'm writing it down. Sky, tree, bluebird. *(Jefferson steps in front of the chair. Light on his face and on Grant's together.)* Mr. Wiggins. Tell them I'm strong. Tell them I'm a man. Sincerely. Jefferson. *(Jefferson slowly sits in the chair. He takes a deep breath, and closes his eyes. The light fades, slowly and gently, on both Jefferson and Grant.)*

End of Play

AUTHOR'S NOTES

Nannan is pronounced *N'-nan,* accent on the *nan.*

Pinchot is pronounced *Pee-sho,* equal accent on both syllables.

Gropé is pronounced *Gro-pay,* accent on the *pay.*

While characters may say they are *going* to the jail tomorrow, they also say they *go'n* talk about God. Going is what they physically mean to do. Go'n is what they personally mean to do. In his novel, Ernest J. Gaines begins the book with the robbery and murder scene. The reader knows that Jefferson is innocent. The audience for the play does not know this, and so it is vital that a very sympathetic young actor play Jefferson. The audience should think from the minute they see him that this young man couldn't kill anyone.

PROPERTY LIST

Handbag containing piece of paper (MISS EMMA)

Package wrapped in newspaper containing pants, long johns, brown shit, 2 pairs socks (MISS EMMA)

Wicker basket containing fried chicken, yams, tea cakes, pralines (MISS EMMA)

Folding chairs (GRANT)

Cardboard box containing package of chalk, 2 battered textbooks (GRANT)

Papers, pens (VIVIAN, GRANT)

2 beers (GRANT)

Penknife (SHERIFF GUIDRY)

Handkerchiefs (SHERIFF GUIDRY, VIVIAN)

Comb (GRANT)

Bag marked "Edwin's" (VIVIAN)

Drinks (GRANT, VIVIAN)

2 one-dollar bills (VIVIAN)

Folder with onion skin carbon copies (PAUL)

Wrapped radio (PAUL, JEFFERSON)

Empty old sacks and bags (GRANT)

Paper sack containing comic books, apples, candy bars (GRANT)

Notebook, pencil, pencil sharpener (GRANT)

Newspaper (PAUL)

Two boxes, tablecloth, 4 spoons, 4 plates, 4 Coca-Colas, pan of gumbo, paper napkins (MISS EMMA, REVEREND AMBROSE)

SOUND EFFECTS

Recorded children's voice-over
Jump and hum of electric generator
Music on the radio